When the Saints Come Marching In

DON LE PARD

American Literary Press, Inc.
Five Star Special Edition
Baltimore, Maryland

When the Saints Come Marching In

Library of Congress
Cataloging in Publication Data
ISBN 1-56167-511-3

Library of Congress Card Catalog Number:
98-89384

Published by

American Literary Press, Inc.
Five Star Special Edition
8019 Belair Road, Suite 10
Baltimore, Maryland 21236

Manufactured in the United States of America

Preface

The loggers were the real American pioneers. They had their own life style. Their lives were always in danger. If they survived the woods, there was always acute alcoholism or barroom brawls.

There was always plenty of timber just over the hill. You could hear the black forest snap and crackle under the influence of the savage cold. It was said the trees would quiver and shake whenever a man walked by them with an axe.

The foreman ruled the camp in the woods, but in the cook shack, the cook was God Almighty. He could become violent at times and slap a man down if he raised his voice. The rule was no talking during the lunch hour.

The camp cook would bake bread over an open

fire. The midday lunch was brought into the woods on a sled. The menu consisted of salt pork and beans along with bread and molasses.

The tea was always strong enough to float an axe.

The life of a lumberjack was simple. In order to be a logger you had to enjoy the wildlife and become a part of the great outdoors.

At that point, he felt the presence of someone behind him. Before he could turn around, a figure grabbed him from behind and thrust a knife into his side. Peter felt the sharp jab as the blade went in. He could sense the pain and felt the hot blood on his fingers. A fatal charge went through his entire body as he slumped to the ground. He thought about his youth. He was stronger than the rest. He could withstand pain. He could endure suffering. He could stand torture. He was tough. He was hard. He could outlast any of them. He was weak now and out of control. The icy snow chilled his face as he blacked out.

Andy made his move. He struck Billy in the nose. Billy responded by pushing him backwards. He fell into a table where four Jacks were sitting. That's all it took. It was like a bell had gone off. The WHOLE place erupted. Fists were flying! Jacks were howling! There was pushing and shoving! Punching and hitting! An uppercut to the chin! A poke in the stomach! A hit on the head! A brass cuspidor banged against the wall! A body was thrown through a window! Chairs were being broken! Tables demolished! The smell of stale beer, dirty sweat, and foul smoke saturated the air..... and still the gala event went on!

REFERENCES

The Autobiography of David Ward

Holy Old Mackinaw by Stewart Holbrook

The Incredible Seney by Lewis Reimann

When Pine Was King by Lewis Reimann

Pioneer Timber King by Dr. Rolland H. Maybee

Pictures from the Otsego County Historical Society

WHEN THE SAINTS COME MARCHING IN

THE LUMBERJACK

He's up in the early morn'
Dressed before the breakfast horn;
In the freezing bitter cold
Is when he works the best I'm told;
A horse's breath hangs in the air
It's furry coat is thick with hair;
An old pine tree that's big and sound
Comes crashing down upon the ground;
It's cut to size and moved away
and loaded on a horse drawn sleigh;
Moving down an icy road
Sliding easy with the load;
The logs are piled high on a hill
Than floated down stream to a mill;
That's the lumberjack we knew
That made the whole event come true.

THE BREAKFAST HOUR

The cook arrives at an early hour
And starts to mix the pancake flour;
He pours the batter on the grill
And flips the cakes with extreme skill;
There's heaps of bacon and sausage too,
Loaded on tables for all to view;
Then the blowing of the horn
Ends the silence of the morn;
Lumberjacks all march inside
Some are big and some are wide;
They move right in and take a seat,
They're happy now 'cause they can eat;
Their mouth's are sealed, not a word,
That's the law, not to be heard.
By the light of a kerosene lamp
That's how it was in a lumber camp.

THE LOG DRIVE

A dam is built along the bank
    to raise the mighty tide,
So when the logs are ready
    they'll take that final ride;
Down the ramp the logs are fired
    and shot out in the drink,
The logs are pretty heavy
    and bigger than you think;
A driver rides them piggyback
    to free the mighty jams,
A dangerous assignment
    he spins and rolls and rams;
After days of sweat and strain
    and everything is still;
The journey is completed
    when the logs are at the mill.

CHAPTER 1

The *Mancelona Herald* was a small town newspaper. It's office was located in a little building on the outskirts of Mancelona. Clark Edwards was the editor, the typesetter and the printer. In fact, he ran the one man newspaper with the help of Mary Johnson who was his only reporter. She was 21 years old and the daughter of a dirt farmer.

One day Clark came up with an idea for a story.

He told Mary, "I want you to take a trip out to the Ward Lumber Camp and interview the big boss. Find out why he went into the lumber business? What it's like being a lumberjack? What they do and how they live? Give me a good human interest story that I can use on the front page."

Mary asked, "What's the owner's name?"

"Let me see now! I've got it right here somewhere! Oh, here it is! His name is David Ward!"

"David Ward! He's probably one of those rich lumber barons who never worked a full day in his life!"

"Well, Mary, talk with him and find out what you can."

Mary smiling, said, "I'll give it a try!"

When Mary approached the lumber camp she found it was nestled in a forest of green pines. Some of the trees were huge. Their trunks were big and stocky. Their green furry branches covered both sides of the road. She felt like she was in a wonderland. A place like she had never been before. The rich green foliage was everywhere. Even the smell was different. The heavenly odor of rich Michigan pine.

She bounced down the road in her buggy until she came to a clearing. There at the side of the road stood a log cabin with a big sign over the door.

Mary read the words out loud, "The Ward Lumber Camp Office."

She stepped down from her buggy and tied the reins of her horse to a post. She then climbed up the steps to the porch and knocked on the door.

Inside David was talking to his foreman Peter Muirhead and his company clerk Gary Olson.

David pointed to a large map on the wall and informed them, "This area by Mud Lake has a large grove of the big pine.

Peter answered, "We could start by the lake and move south!"

Gary added, "If we cleared that area out we

would have a place to store the logs!"

David agreed, "Sounds good to me. How about you, Peter?"

Peter acknowledged, "Yeah! I think it will work!"

All three of the men looked up when the knock came on the door.

Gary shouted, "I'll get it!"

His leather boots hammered away on the hardwood floor as he moved up to the big oak door. He turned the knob to open it.

The men all stood silent as they looked down on the young girl standing in the doorway.

David spoke up, "Is there something we can help you with?"

Mary replied, "Yes! I'm from the *Mancelona Herald*! I'm Mary Johnson, a newspaper reporter, and I'd like to get a story about your lumbercamp!"

David offered his hand to her and added, "Come inside child! I'm David Ward. You find a chair over there and I'll be glad to talk with you."

Mary remarked, "Much obliged."

After she sat down she opened a small notebook. A pencil came out of her pocket and she looked up into David's face.

David turned to his companions and informed them, "You men can start working on that project!"

The two men nodded and left the room.

David then settled down in his chair behind his desk and asked, "Where do you want me to start?"

Mary thought for a minute and then responded, "Well, maybe at the beginning! When did you first become interested in the lumber business?"

David leaned back in his chair and started out, "Well, it all started many years ago..."

CHAPTER 2

One morning my father told me we were going to move to Michigan to live. I was both thrilled and excited. In fact, I was tickled pink. Imagine, going into a virgin state. One that had not yet been explored. One with vast wilderness. One with awesome wild life. The dark country. Maybe I'd be attacked by a bear or scalped by an Indian. The thought was overwhelming. It was sensational. We were going to live in the wilds of Michigan.

I was so excited I couldn't sleep that night. I rolled and tossed, and when I finally dozed off, I saw a big Indian brave with war paint on his face. He was standing right over me. He raised a tomahawk high in the air and was about to bring it down when I heard another sound. It was the shaking noise of a rattlesnake. It was all coiled up ready to strike. When it's fangs finally came at me everything went black. Then, a wolf appeared. He was sitting high on a hill with a pale moon shining behind him. He pointed his head straight up into the heavens and let out a blood curdling howl. Then from out of nowhere came a huge black bear. Its big mouth opened up wide and when its sharp teeth were about to tear at my flesh, I jumped out of bed and ran right into the arms of my mother.

She remarked, "Good! I'm glad you're up! We've got a lot to do today!"

I was fourteen at the time when my father left Keene, New York, and took my mother, my two sisters and myself up into the state of Michigan.

The year was 1836 and we found that Michigan had not yet joined the Union. It seems that the legislature had not received the proper number of votes.

My father bought a horse for our journey. My sister Charen named him "Ned." That's how the animal got his name. On our first night out we stayed with a friend of the family, Kenneth Partridge, who lived on his own "Partridge Hill." We started right out the next morning happy and in good spirits. We then learned that our mother had a premonition of dying and being buried along the way.

The second night we stayed with a friend of my father, Charlie Brown, at Westport on Lake Champlain. It was a beautiful lake, we all agreed.

The third day we arrived at the Michigan border. When we crossed over into Michigan we found we were in the city of Detroit. The streets were all dirt. Jefferson Avenue was very muddy. The people milling around the streets were of French and

Indian descent. The sidewalks were made of wooden planks inserted endways. Because this was a waterfront town, the fields were all damp with a marshy soil. We observed some old apple trees growing along the roadway. A man with a wide nose said they were a hundred years old. They had been planted by Chief Pontiac back there in the year 1700. They did look old and ugly.

The third night we stayed at a hotel in Detroit called the Mansion House located on Woodbridge street by the dock.

I thought Michigan would be wild and wooly. Tough and dangerous. I was disappointed. I anticipated more action. Bring on the cowboys and Indians! I craved activity. I required excitement. It was too quiet! Too peaceful! Too tame!

It was all right for my father. He was a surveyor. He enjoyed studying the woods and the plant life. The foliage and the leafage. He observed the texture and the development of the vegetation.

But for me, I was different. I CRAVED excitement. I wanted something to happen. I had a WILD surge of energy flowing through my veins.

We made our way out of the city and into the country. It was almost like they had rolled out the green carpet, just for us. The huge trees reached high into the heavens. We saw oak, elm and black ash. Their branches formed a cover over our pathway. Our Indian pony trail lacked a pattern. It went in all directions, around trees, up hills, and down gullies. It was a welcome change that broke the monotony.

The sun finally disappeared and then the rain came. A heavy downpour that seemed to drench everything. A downpour so heavy it cleansed our souls. It covered the ground deep down under, saturating our clothing and soaking us to the skin. The heavens let go like a babbling brook overflowing its banks. It washed away our very existence. The raindrops spattered on old Ned like an open shower running down his sides. It made little rivers running in all directions. The water drops spattered as they hit the puddles. The dirt turned to mud. The grass turned to a spongy water bed in a garden.

Old Ned carried on aimlessly into the interior. We were doing well until we moved up a small hill and the wagon suddenly stopped. A wheel was stuck in the mud. Everybody jumped out to free the pesky sprocket. We all pushed together. On the second try I slipped. I fell headlong into a pool of mud. Shirt, pants and all of me soaked to the skin. An ooey-gooey mess that I would never live down. It did do one thing for me. It seemed to take the starch out of my sails. It slowed me down.

The rain finally stopped and the sun brightened up the forest green.

My father held up his hand and ordered, "We'll stop here for lunch!"

The wagon pulled to a stop and we all piled out

for some nourishment. My sisters spread out a blanket for a tablecloth. The bread was cut and we all enjoyed sandwiches made with Mom's blueberry jelly. We washed it down with some warm tea.

After lunch we were back on the trail again. This time we came across a big meadow full of yellow daisies. Then, it seems from out of the blue, came a man with a black beard riding on a chestnut horse.

My father flagged him down and yelled, "Is this the right trail to Newport?"

The man swung his mount around and reported, "Yeah! Right on down the trail. You can't miss it!"

"Much obliged!" my father said as he shook up the reins to old Ned and we moved on down the trail.

The man slapped the reins against his animal's rump and rode off.

When we arrived in Newport we were almost there. The last three miles were the longest. Then, as slick as you please, my Dad took us right into the yard of a red French farm house and that was it. The journey was over and we were finally home. We were now Michiganders.

CHAPTER 3

We started right out the next day planting a vegetable garden. We first had to clear the land. We removed the stumps, small trees and the underbrush. We used old Ned to help plow up the ground. Then, after raking the soil we were ready for planting. My sisters made a game of it.

Charen spouted off, "I bet I can finish my row first!"

Emma answered, "You're on!"

We kept the soil watered and after about ten days the tiny green sprouts started popping out of the ground.

Charen had a problem and remarked, "Why are some of your carrot tops missing, David?"

Emma added, "Yeah, he probably forgot to plant the seeds!"

They both laughed and my face got red.

I was determined to catch the animal that was devouring my carrot tops. I was puzzled and felt cheated. Then, one day as the sun was coming up, I saw the creature. It appeared to be a big black cat that was chewing away at my carrot tops. I ran out of the house to chase the scoundrel away. I started swinging my arms and yelling loudly. Then I saw the white streak. It was a beautiful white strip that went all the way down the rascal's back. At that moment I heard a hissing sound, felt the spray and smelled the odor. It was a skunk all right, and I was his victim. Even after a bath, the odor remained. I had to burn my clothing, and my family requested that I keep to myself.

I decided to go fishing. The little stream that ran right through our back yard looked like an ideal spot. In the shadow of an old oak tree I dug for worms. I got some big night crawlers. Then I cut a branch for a pole, got some string for a line, and I was going fishing.

When I got to the stream, I found a spot by a big elm. Just as I was baiting my hook I heard a strange sound. It was the shaking of a rattlesnake. I could see he was all coiled up ready to strike. I swung my bucket of worms around just as his fangs came at me. He buried them right in the wooden bucket. To this day his fangs are still there in that bucket. I never went fishing in that place again.

The next day I decided to go into Newport for some excitement. That's when I met Jeffery Smith.

We were talking and he asked, "David! We're going to raid Old Man Montigue's apple orchard tonight. Do you want to come along?"

His brother Joey added, "He's got a shotgun

but we're not afraid!"

I hesitated and then decided, "Sure! Why not! It might be fun!"

Jeffery then announced, "We'll meet at the Town hall at midnight."

It was a bright moonlit night when we climbed over the orchard fence. I was chewing on an apple when Old Sam, the farmer's hound dog, got our scent. He opened up with the most ungodly howl you ever heard. I'm sure it woke the dead. Of course, we all froze in our tracks. It was then that the back door flew open and Mr. Montigue came flying out in his red long johns. The apple I was chewing on got stuck in my throat.

His big bass voice boomed out, "All right you kids! Stay right where ya' are! I'll fill ya' full of buckshot if ya' move!"

At that point the whole bunch scattered. He pointed the gun barrel up to the heavens and pulled the trigger. Apples, branches and leaves came down in all directions. It was like a cannon had gone off at the Battle of Bull Run.

He bellered out, "I told you kids not to move! Stay right where ya' are! So help me, I swear, if you move I'll fill ya' full of buckshot!"

My mouth suddenly became very dry, but I decided to speak, "I'm David Ward, and I'm sorry I stole your apples. I just moved here from New York. I meant no harm!"

Mr. Montigue, still pointing the gun at me,

sounded off, "So, I've got a live one! Ya' didn't run! Ya' got yourself caught! Tell me! Do ya' know who them there other kids are?"

"No sir!" I responded, "I never saw them before today and I'll probably never see them again!"

Mr. Montigue lowered the barrel of his shotgun to the ground and then explained, "I'll tell ya' what I'm gonna' do. Since you're new around these parts I'll let cha' go. Providin' one thing. For stealing my apples I got some chores you can perform. Yes siree! I know that cow manure don't smell none too good, but I wantcha' to clean out my stable. I've got a pitchfork that's jest your size and it's waitin' fer ya'. Go on home now and git some sleep and I'll see ya' back here first thing in the mornin'!"

My shirt felt cold and damp as I walked home that night. I returned the next day and cleaned out his stable. I never stole apples again.

A pool of water, when quiet and still, is like a looking glass. It shows your reflection. The only problem was when I looked down into the water another face appeared. It was the face of a big Indian, and he was sitting right next to me. I swallowed deeply and couldn't believe my eyes. Where had he come from, and how did he get here? I heard no sound.

He held out a piece of beef jerky in the palm of

his hand. He offered it to me. I took it and placed it in my mouth. It was hard and dry. I turned it over slowly as I gasped for air.

His tanned face lit up, and he knew I was having trouble.

"Gitchee!" he blurted out, which meant trouble.

I nodded my head yes. He motioned for me to chew with my teeth. I ground away trying to make it smaller, and I finally succeeded.

That was the first time I met Running Squirrel. I liked his spirit and his good ideas.

He was wearing a dusty buckskinned jacket, and his black hair was in braids. His moccasins scuffed along in the light sand as he walked. He was a likeable fellow and my friend. I was fascinated by his gestures and the way he moved.

He pulled out a big jackknife and held it in the palm of his hand. He then pulled open the blade and showed me how it could cut a little twig. He made a little growl in his throat telling me it was good. I nodded back that I agreed.

He took my arm and we moved over to a little pile of stones. He reached down and picked up a small pebble. On closer observation I could see that it was a small arrowhead, the type used for an Indian arrow. I marvelled at the way it was made.

He pointed up in the sky at a big eagle flying overhead. He pointed over to a large nest in the top of a tall tree.

He was telling me that was the bird's home.

He pointed to his lips for me to be quiet. We moved on over to a large tree and peered around its trunk. There was a doe standing there feeding on the buds of a tree. He put his hand on his stomach informing me that the deer was pregnant and was about to have a fawn. I nodded that I understood.

I had to go on a surveying trip with my Dad. I was gone for about two months. When I returned, I found out that Running Squirrel had moved away. I never saw him again.

CHAPTER 4

One evening after supper, while my father, Nathan, was smoking his pipe, he glanced over at me and explained, "You know son, I'm going on a surveying trip tomorrow, and I want you to come along."

I was thrilled and answered, "All right, Dad, I'd like that."

"There's going to be a great deal of walking involved but I think you can handle it."

"Yeah, Dad, I can handle it!"

"We'll pack our backpacks tonight, so we can leave first thing in the morning."

I couldn't sleep that night. I laid in bed and thought of how great it would be working with my Dad. We'd be going though green forests of white pine which would be way out there in the wilderness. We'd be surveying new lands and claiming them for our own. It would be a dream come true.

The next morning I met my father at the breakfast table. He was already dressed and ready to go. After breakfast we both put on our mackinaws, slipped into our backpacks, and then we were gone.

There was a chill in the air as we left the house. The tinted leaves had changed the woods. They were different colors now. Some of the maples were glowing red. Their different shades stood out against the sky. A painter's brush dominated the scene splashing on bright yellow and orange. The countryside was turned into a fancy magic land. Their brightness lighted up our woodland path. The leaves seemed to know their impending fate as a gentle breeze dropped them to the ground. It was autumn all right, and it created a new universe. A fantasy to remember. A delusion that came to life. We hiked on down the path and made our way out of town.

My father told me to observe the many large tracts of pine along the way and to remember where they were located.

We hiked all morning and finally arrived at the town of Redford. My father paused in front of a house with a white picket fence running it. We both noticed a sign on a post that read "Judge Peter Smith". I followed my Dad through the gate and up the steps where he used the doorknocker.

It wasn't long before the judge opened the door and greeted us with, "Good morning! Come on in!"

We all moved into his study and found chairs in front of a big oak desk.

17

My father hesitated and then asked, "Do you want to see me?"

Judge Smith smiled and acknowledged, "I SURE do! I have a proposition for you!"

My Dad looked puzzled and confused, "What do you have in mind?"

"Look," the judge ordered as he unrolled a big map and placed it on his desk. "Here's a map of the central section of Michigan." Jabbing his finger down on the map he demanded, "This is the virgin pine I want! Are you familiar with it?"

"Yes," my father complied, "I know about where that's located!"

"Good," the judge responded. "Now, I'm prepared to give you two thousand dollars, for which, I want you to locate, select, and buy the best darn virgin pine you can find!"

My Dad smiled and assured, "Yeah! I can do that!"

"Great!" the judge confirmed, "Now, I expect you to keep one quarter of the land as payment for your services!"

My Dad stood up with approval, "That sounds fair enough!"

"Fine!" the judge went on, "Now, I have a receipt drawn up for you to sign for the two thousand dollars."

My father noticed that there was nothing on the receipt for his services, but trusting the judge he signed the paper anyway.

After we left the judge's house we traveled through the woods in silence. I looked down at the list of sightings I had been recording. I counted two large tracts of good white pine. The trees were a healthy green color with soft pine needles. Finally, we came to a clearing in the woods where there was a beautiful meadow. The grass was a blue green color with a little brook running through it.

My Dad stared at a big tree in the distance for a minute and then nodded his head and decided, "We'll camp here for the night."

I was very happy to hear that because my legs were tired.

My father slipped off his backpack and pulled out a small tin pail and pushed it in my direction.

"You get some water and I'll build a fire!"

I nodded and walked on down the path to the brook. When I approached the water I heard a big bird making a crazy squawking sound. It was a large black crane that slapped its huge wings against the water as it left the area. It seemed to be in a hurry.

I dropped the pail into the water and was about to scoop it up when I heard another sound. It was the snarl of a wolf coming from the opposite bank. I yanked the pail out of the water and started pounding my feet back to camp.

As I moved, I yelled, "Wolf! Wolf! There's a wolf!"

I could feel his hot breath and the surge of his

savage power. He was snapping and pawing at my legs. My father, working with the fire, swung around with a burning stick. He poked it into the face of the charging animal. The wolf stopped short, drew back and then disappeared into the underbrush. I fell on the ground exhausted. I was shaking. I was half-crying. I was scared out of my mind. I had been attacked by a beast that had almost eaten me alive!

My Dad, who was also shaking, suggested, "Come on, let's get some supper!"

We ate our food in silence.

After I finished an apple, I asked, "I guess he's gone?"

My father, after sipping on his tea, answered, "Don't count on it!"

My Dad was right because, as the sun began to set, the gray dog was back. This time he brought along more of his family. There were at least a dozen now. They were everywhere circling our camp like Indians on a pow wow. Their groans and snarls were like a verbal chant in a ceremony for a human sacrifice.

From the light of our camp fire we could see their red eyes and white fangs beckoning to us. They were hungry all right, and they were moving in for the kill. My skin began to crawl, and I broke out in a cold sweat. My life didn't mean much anymore. What a terrible way to die. The end would come soon. I could feel their teeth tearing away at my flesh. I could feel my very soul being sucked out of my body. This would be the end. There was no other way. This was our final hour. I knew we would never make it through the night.

Finally, there was a change in plans. The good Lord had heard our prayers. There was hope again. The crisis was over. We had survived. When the sun came up, the wolves were gone. They had disappeared. The woods were quiet again, and everything was back to normal.

I spoke to Him. I said, "Thank you, Lord, for saving our lives and giving us another chance to live again."

CHAPTER 5

I worked with my father in seeking out timber for the judge. We both traveled though swamps, hills and over vast mountain ranges. Finally, we came to a region of fine hemlock and mountain spruce. We had found the pine for the judge right here in Elk Creek.

The next job was to record it. We went to the site and set up our solar compass. We took a sighting at the center of the tract. Then we made another sighting at the far end. We paced off the distance and recorded it. We did the same in the opposite direction. After calculating our findings, we had our facts complete. Our next step was to record our prize purchase at the U.S. Land office in Detroit.

We were both tired and hungry when we arrived in Detroit. The trip had been hard on my legs, and my feet were very sore. We ate a good supper and then stayed overnight in the Mansion House Hotel where we had stayed before.

When we woke up the next morning we were

eager to make the purchase. The U.S. Land office was located in an old Detroit City Hall building. When we entered the room, we saw a little old man wearing tiny rimmed glasses. He was perched up on a high stool behind a big oak desk. He wore a white shirt with black armbands above his elbows.

He looked up at us and in a little squeaky voice asked, "Can I help you?"

My father pushed the wrinkled paper over to him and said, "We want to file a claim!"

The little man looked at the paper in puzzlement. Then he pulled out a huge black book from a bookcase. He spread the ledger open on his desk in front of him. After turning several pages, he moved his fingers down a list of entries.

When he finally arrived at the proper place, he remarked, "Oh, here we are!"

We both stared in amazement.

He picked up a pen and after dipping it into an inkwell made an entry as he spoke, "Town 29, North Range 4 and 5 West."

Nathan explained, "I wish to make two purchases because a quarter of the land belongs to me for my services."

The little man looked up over his glasses and said, "No problem!"

My father counted out the proper money and then received two Bill of Sales.

After we left the Land office, we went to the Post office where my father mailed the largest bill of sale to the judge. Our work was completed now, so we could start home.

When we arrived home, some days later, we found a telegram was waiting for my Dad. It was from Gerrit Smith, the son of the judge. My father was shocked when he found out that the judge had passed away due to a heart attack. Gerrit explained that he was the Executor of his father's estate and wanted the other Bill of Sale for Elk Creek. My father wrote back and explained that the property did not belong to the judge because it was payment for his services. Gerrit refused to accept the explanation and threatened to sue. My father, having no alternative, sent his bill of sale to him for the property.

I decided to take a little time off from surveying, so I got a job as storekeeper at Burt's General Store. One day when I was sweeping the floor, Robert Duval, dressed in buckskins, came into the store.

"Hey, young man! Have you got any baked beans?" Robert uttered.

I responded, "Yeah! They're over there by the tomatoes."

"Do you like working in a store?"

"Yeah. It's all right."

"Well, it's not for me. I'm an outdoor man! I like being out in the woods. I've got my traps set all around this area!"

"You're a trapper?"

"Yup! That's what I do."

"I've never met a fur trapper before!"

"Well, I'm going to check my traps when I leave here. You can come along if you wanta'."

"Oh, I'd like that!"

I finished my work at the store and then left with Robert to go into the woods.

We walked over hills and through valleys where I had never been before. There were hidden places behind rocks and near caves where Robert had placed his traps. I wondered how he could remember where they all were.

We were traveling through a bushy area when Robert suddenly grabbed my arm. He pointed down to the ground at a large foot print. It was a fresh track of a bear. Before we could move, a big black hairy object loomed up in front of us. It was a bear all right, and she was scratching her back on the bark of a tree. She was really enjoying herself. Her huge front legs hung down as she continued her exercise. Then, we saw the two cubs.

Robert whispered, "Thank God, the wind is in another direction. She hasn't got our scent yet!"

We both stood there very still trying to figure out what to do next.

Robert whispered again, "That's about the worst thing that could happen to us. A bear with two cubs. She'll be meaner than sin! If they'd only just go away!"

The woods became real still. I tried hard not to breathe heavy. The only sound was the wind blowing through the soft pine needles. Suddenly the big animal stood up on its hind legs. She was huge, and she was restless. She finally got our scent and opened her big mouth and let out a blood curdling growl. Robert accidentally touched the trigger on his rifle. The sound echoed through the woods. My ears were ringing, and my head was pounding from the concussion.

The bear, stunned by the explosion, stood paralyzed by a tree.

Robert started running, and I was right behind him. It seems when you're scared you inherit extreme power. Our feet went hammering down the path knocking down heavy ferns and flattening thick underbrush.

Robert pointed to a tree and shouted, "Let's climb that baby!"

Without hesitation, we both grabbed the first branch and drew ourselves up. Feverishly, our arms hugged the trunk for dear life. We hoped the bear wouldn't decide to climb the same tree. With hearts pounding and our lungs gasping for air, we finally settled down.

There are certain characteristics about a bear. They have a keen sense of smell. Their weight is from four to six hundred pounds. They can climb trees. They like honey, berries, and fish. They enjoy a bath in a stream, and they are fast runners. The mother bear will also forget her anger when she finds out her cubs are no longer in danger.

Finally, we looked down and saw the two cubs come walking down the path with the mother bear right behind them. They walked right past our tree and moved on out into the woods. This meant that we were no longer in danger. We were no longer a threat to the mother bear.

Robert gave me the thumbs up for victory. I repeated the same gesture.

Robert leaned over and informed me, "I think they're gone. We can climb down now."

I had heard many stories about bears. How their front legs were extremely powerful. If they ever struck you with their claws they could rip your arm right off.

We had met a bear face to face, and we had survived. We were both grateful and thankful to be alive.

CHAPTER 6

My Uncle Samuel, who couldn't read or write, bellered out, "I don't need no danged school to give me any learnin'! I built my shippin' business into a roarin' success without the help of any fancy lessons. And another thing! I'm not sending my two daughters into that tha' fancy schoolhouse. No sir, it ain't fer me!"

My Uncle Sam was very well off. He owned two shipping boats and had stock in a third. He had just built a new home and was completely out of debt. We were very poor, and my father ran a tab at Burt's General Store. It was so we could buy food when we didn't have the money. I stopped by the store one day to buy some butter and eggs.

When Samuel heard me ask for credit he exploded, "Hey Burt! You ain't agonna' give that kid any credit are ya'? Why that thar' family is as poor as dirt! You'll never git your money! You're takin' an awful chance!"

Burt remembered me when I was working for him and knew it wasn't true.

On my way home I passed by Samuel's house. I saw the big garden he had and how the vegetables were rotting on the vines. I thought what a waste. What a treat it would have been to have that food on our supper table before it spoiled.

It was 1839 when my father finally did get some surveying work which meant no more stewed peas for supper. Times were tough, and I took a job cleaning out a stable for our neighbor. I got up at five o'clock in the morning to give his horses fresh straw before I went to school.

The one room schoolhouse always seemed over-crowded. There were kids of all ages learning different subjects at the same time.

Since I could both read and write, Mrs. Armstrong, the school marm, asked me if I would mind helping some of the slow learners.

I replied, "Of course, I would be glad to help!"

I could see some of the problems the kids were having with their studies. Reading was indeed very difficult for some kids. They couldn't remember the simple words. Spelling was a little easier. They could sound out the different letters. That is, if they could remember the sounds. Then, mathematics was a whole different thing. They just had to learn their time tables.

When their parents couldn't read or write, it made things difficult for the kids.

One day Mrs. Armstrong spoke to the village council.

She said, "I want to inform you that I'll be leaving. I have taken another teaching assignment in Carson City. I do recommend that you might hire David as a temporary instructor until a new teacher can be found."

That's how I got my first teaching job.

They called me the Little Yankee Schoolmaster. I did my best to prove myself as a teacher. I tried different techniques. I was sincere about their learning. I did improve their test scores and finally saw some results. They were learning to read and write. My skills were working.

After two years the village council finally decided to replace me with another teacher. In that period of time, I had applied for a teacher's degree at the University of Michigan and received my diploma. I had two professions now. A surveyor and the other as a teacher.

As a teacher, they paid me ten dollars a month plus board. That meant I had to live around with the different families. I did refuse living with the Yodeling Johnny family. For some reason his Swiss singing didn't agree with me.

CHAPTER 7

He was a tall lanky fellow who was six-foot-four with a good disposition. That was John Baily, who was to be my next partner on my surveying trip into the white pine country of Michigan.

Our mission was to locate and purchase a rich tract of virgin pine located in the heart of the Otsego Valley. Our sponsor was William Howard and Associates of Detroit. We were informed that the Soo Canal Explorers were also interested in the same tract of land. Our goal was to get there ahead of them and make the purchase.

When I looked through the frosted window glass of our cabin the temperature gauge read thirty degrees below zero. I shuddered to think of having to go out in all that mess. I shrugged my shoulders and said there's just one thing to do.

I slipped into my mackinaw and then strapped on my hundred pound backpack. John did the same.

I was smiling when I spoke, "Nice morning!"

John answered back, "Couldn't be better!"

After we put on our fur hats and pulled on our

mittens we were both ready to meet the cold challenge. The air was brisk and frosted our lungs. I stepped out onto a large snowbank and found that it supported my weight.

My breath hung in the air as I spoke, "Can you imagine that? I can walk on it! Here! Let me take your hand!"

John poked his mitten out at me and I helped him up .

"I'd never believe that it could hold me," John said as he pushed his feet along in the snow.

We were finally on our way as our boots crunched in the heavy snow. It wasn't Alaska but Michigan in the month of March. We both knew it wouldn't be easy. It never was.

I thought about John Milton, the Federal Surveyor, who had tipped me off about the excellent cork pine that we would find one and a half miles west of Otsego Lake. And yes, I mustn't forget about Addison Brewer and the Soo Canal explorers who had planned an expedition to the same place on April 5th. That's why I had planned to leave earlier. Hey, nobody was going to get there ahead of us, nobody.

Day after day we trudged on through the white stuff breaking a trail in the dense snow. At times it seemed like a bad dream. Every snowbank looked alike. Our compass was our only guide. When we arrived at the Tittabawasee River, we found it was still frozen over. We walked on down the river and passed the town of Midland. We went on through the spruce pine plains to Bradford Lake.

We didn't want the Soo agents to know that we were ahead of them so we camped twenty rods off the main path every night.

When we arrived at our final destination, the healthy crop of pines were the best I had ever seen. We did find that the Federal Surveyors had been inaccurate in their calculations. We had to correct several mistakes that they had made. It seemed like we worked forever pacing out the footage and writing down measurements. The hours were long, and the days seemed to go on forever. Our calculations showed sixteen thousand acres in Town 29 and 30 North and Range 3 and 4 West.

Our work was completed now, so we could start back.

On the twenty-first day of April we came across the trail of the Soo agents. It happened a few miles north of Frederic when we met two men carrying heavy backpacks.

I approached them and spoke up, "Hello! We seem to be lost. Can you tell us where we can find the trail to the Tobacco River?"

A little man with a black beard answered, "Hold on. We've got a map right here."

He took off his backpack and pulled out a well worn piece of paper.

He pointed to the map and explained, "We're right here now and if you go down the river around this curve you should find the trail right there.

I answered, "Much obliged for your help!"

The bearded man continued, "No problem! You see that funny mark on the map? Well, that's the place where we left our canoe. We hid it in the bushes where nobody would find it. It has all our provisions in it for our trip back."

I remarked, "That's interesting. Thanks again!"

The man waved good-bye and said, "No trouble! Glad we could help!"

After we walked down the path a ways, I smiled and looked over at John and confessed, "We want to thank you for your help and especially for the location of your canoe and the supplies."

John answered, "Yeah, that's a gift from heaven!"

Looking at the water I thought out loud, "We got to find a way to get down that river. We'll have to build a raft!"

John replied, "I had the same idea."

We tied some logs together with twine and then dragged them out onto the water's edge. We floated down the river until we came to the spot where the canoe was hidden. We found the food supplies under the boat just like the man said, so we celebrated. What do you know? There was a jug of applejack whisky. Wow! Did that have a kick! Everything began to look rosy. The clouds started moving around in the heavens and the trees began dancing. Even the ground seemed to be moving.

John was doing the Merry Widow waltz, and I broke out with Davy Crockett. The two songs didn't mix, but we had a ball anyway. John grabbed up a little tree and was using it as his dancing partner. I started jumping around with a chicken reel. Finally, my legs gave out, and I had to rest. That's when we both must have dozed off. When I heard the outcry of a black crow, I opened up my eyes. John was sleeping soundly near by. I shook him and said we better move on. We both climbed into their canoe and paddled our way down the Titabawassee River to Saginaw.

When we arrived in Saginaw, the plan was for me to rent a horse and buggy while John would find a restaurant where we could eat our final meal. I sent a wire from the telegraph office to our sponsor, William Howard of Detroit. I informed him to have warrants, money, and a fresh horse ready when I arrived. After a couple of Delmonico steaks, we were both ready for the big night ride.

I dressed up in my Sunday best, climbed into the buggy with John, and we both rode out of the city in the darkness. It took a while before our eyes became adjusted to the black of night. It was black as ink. Our eyes started playing tricks. The shadows took on objects. Strange figures were standing in the woods. A tall ghost stood along the roadside. The Devil himself was by a tree. Bats flew across our path. The night was indeed spooky. The whole countryside was haunted. The horse knew the way so we both took a catnap as we jiggled on down the dirt road.

When we arrived in Pontiac, John finally announced, "Well, this is where I leave you. I'm heading for Port Huron. I'm glad I was part of this wild land race."

I smiled and agreed, "It has been a tough one."

We both shook hands, and I watched as John walked away. I would be traveling down the dark road all alone now.

When I arrived in Detroit, William was there to greet me.

He helped me down from the buggy and said, "You are making good time! I have everything that you requested. In the satchel you'll find the money and the land warrants you asked for."

I went over and rubbed the horse's nose and informed him, "It's best I leave right away!"

"Don't you think you'd better get some sleep?" William suggested.

I shrugged my shoulders and answered, "There'll be plenty of time for sleep when it's over."

I climbed up into the new buggy, waved my hand, and away I went. I drove all night and part of the next day and arrived in Ionia at a little past five.

The land office clerk welcomed me, "Hello Sonny! Wat'cha got?"

"I've got some warrants and money. I want to

purchase some land."

"Well, I'll tell ya' Sonny, the office is closed."

"But, I've been riding all night!"

"Well, I'll tell ya' what I'm gonna' do. I'll put your warrants and money in the safe and tomorrow you can make the purchase. You'll still have first choice. That's the rule, you know."

"I guess that's the only way to handle it!"

"Why don't you get a good night's sleep. You look tired!"

I climbed back into my buggy and headed for a hotel.

The sun was shining brightly when I opened up my eyes the next morning. I was lost for a minute, but then I remembered the warrants. I had to get them recorded right away. I slid out of bed and started getting dressed. I had to get to the land office before the Soo agents.

When I got to the land office, the clerk was sitting in a chair on the porch.

He got up and told me, "I've been waiting for you. Come on inside, and we'll get your warrants recorded."

I followed him inside.

We struggled for an hour working on the records.

Finally, all the land was recorded, and the money was paid. I walked out of the Federal Land office with a bill of sale in my pocket. I had won the race.

Twenty minutes after I left, a representative from the Soo Canal explorers arrived. His horse was covered with a heavy white sweat.

When he presented his list of land to be recorded, the clerk shook his head and explained, "I am sorry, but all that land has been purchased. That land is no longer for sale."

The man's face was white as he turned around and walked out of the land office. When he got outside, he looked down at his horse that was laying on the ground. It was dying from exhaustion.

Six weeks after the great race, I received a letter from the land office in Ionia. They informed me that all my land purchases had been cancelled. I would have to do it all over again by recording my findings at a land office in Cheboygan.

CHAPTER 8

When I wasn't teaching I was out in the woods surveying. I was being recognized for my expertise in the field of Surveying. A number of my business associates were the Rust Brothers, two members of the Michigan Central Railroad and William Howard of Detroit.

I found my lungs were frosted after I returned from one of my surveying trips. I had several bad attacks of coughing. My lungs were weak, and I developed a case of pleurisy. After I was down in bed for several days, I decided to find out more about my condition. I started to read all the doctor's books I could find. I also attended a series of readings by Dr. Steinbeck in Ann Arbor. In fact, I became so involved and intrigued by my condition that I decided to study the field of medicine.

On my many trips to Ann Arbor, I met Elizabeth Perkins. She was studying to be a nurse, and we attended many of the same readings. Dr. Steinbeck, who was my advisor, encouraged me to take the medical examination. With the support of

Elizabeth, I got through the course. After many more lectures and considerable study, I finally passed the examination and received my medical degree. It was then that I married Elizabeth.

After a short honeymoon Elizabeth returned back home with me to live. I had a large wall map hanging in my study where I circled the different properties and land that I owned. When Elizabeth saw the map, she was very impressed.

She spoke up, "Do you own all that land? All those woods? All that timber? Why don't you open up your own lumber camp? With that much land you ought to turn it into income property.

I replied, "Me? Open up a lumber camp? I never thought about it before. I am just a teacher and a simple surveyor. That's what I do for a living. I've always worked for someone else. I never dreamed of being my own boss."

She smiled and suggested, "You must know of someone you could talk to? Someone who could help? Someone who could get you started?"

I felt puzzled and then answered, "Sure, I've worked with plenty of big men, most of them millionaires. Maybe you're right. Maybe I should follow this through. Let me see now, I could talk with Charley Dwight. He owns a big logging camp in Frederic. Hmm...I'll pay him a visit."

CHAPTER 9

The next day I paid my good friend Charley Dwight a visit. He ran the Dwight Lumber Camp about fifty miles from where I lived.

When I approached his property, I noticed there was a big fence running around the camp. As I drove my buggy up to the front gate, a big lanky fellow approached me.

He was very serious as he informed me, "This is private property."

I smiled and answered, "I know. I'm a friend of Charley Dwight, and I want to pay him a visit."

The man said, "Well, you go on down to that little house up ahead. He's in his office right now."

I thanked the man and moved on. When I came to the building, I got out of my buggy and tied the reins of my horse to a hitching post. When I knocked on the door, a voice inside told me to enter. As I pushed open the door, I saw Charley sitting at his desk.

"David, you old goat. Glad to see you," he remarked.

I moved over to his desk and shook his hand.

"What brings you to this part of the woods?" he asked, getting to his feet.

"I need someone to talk to," I confessed as I sat down in a chair.

He pointed to all the papers on his desk and explained, "I was just checking on my supplies. What's on your mind?"

I leaned over the desk and continued, "I've been buying land for years and now I want to turn it into a profit."

He looked puzzled for a minute and then remarked, "What do you mean by that?"

"I'd like to open up my own lumber camp. I'll need some advice."

He looked confused for a minute but then smiled and advised, "You won't have any trouble. You'll do all right!"

"I know, but where do I start?"

"Well, first off you'll need a good foreman and I have just the man for you. You see, it so happens I have two at the present time, and I only need one."

"You mean you'll give me one of your foreman?"

"This man knows the woods. Believe me, he'll get the job done for you."

I was both grateful and thankful.

Charley stood up and reported, "Logging is a lot different now than it used to be. The band saw has made the difference. The silver blade can chew 'em up and grind 'em through. The silver steel ribbon is a welcome sight. It has changed the logger's life. It has improved his working conditions. It has transformed the woods into a working sawmill. The transition was overnight. Now, it's a pleasure working in the woods. Getting the job done in half the time. That's progress I guess."

I smiled and answered, "I agree."

He cleared his throat and then went on, "Now, about that foreman. He's probably just finished his breakfast. I'll catch him before he goes out into the woods."

I sat there with the feeling of contentment. A heavy weight had been taken off my shoulders. I was encouraged now. My dreams had been answered. All my doubts were gone. I was sure now that I was doing the right thing.

After I met foreman Peter Muirhead, Charley showed me around. We visited the bunkhouse, the cookshack, and then he gave a tour of the grounds. He showed me where everything was and how everything worked. He took me to the spot where his jacks were felling a big tree. He showed me how they loaded the big logs and moved them into storage. He even showed me how the water crew coated the roads with ice so the huge sleds would move freely.

I left the Dwight Lumber Camp on a new high. I felt pleased and contented. Delighted and happy. Thrilled and excited. I couldn't wait to open my own lumber camp.

CHAPTER 10

Danny O'Brien was looking at the prettiest girl he'd ever seen. She held out her hand to him which he took and drew her close. He was about to kiss her when the breakfast horn sounded. He opened his eyes and stared up at the wooden ceiling. Where was he? What was happening? Everything was different. Everything was strange. Then, when he saw the wooden double decker bunks, all standing in a row, he remembered where he was.

The breakfast horn had sounded and he had better get up for breakfast. He slid his feet out from under the warm blankets on to the cold floor. He poked his arms into his woolen shirt and pushed his feet into his heavy pants. After he drew up his suspenders he pulled on his socks and boots. Now, he was ready. He slipped into his mackinaw as he went out the door.

It was his first day on the job as a lumberjack helper.

The breakfast line had already formed outside the cookshack. There were jacks of all sizes. Some big. Some small. Some fat and some wide.

Danny could smell the sausage and the bacon. There were steaming stacks of hot cakes sitting on the tables. Then, the second sound of the horn, and they all marched inside.

He found a seat at a wooden table and filled his tin plate with the precious food. A smear of butter along with all that maple syrup made them go down real easy.

It was a meal fit for a king. They were all kings. Kings of the jungle of ice and snow. Lumberjacks in the camp of David Ward.

Then came the cold air after the breakfast hour when they all climbed aboard the sleigh. The huge Belgian horses stomping their hoofs in anticipation. The breath of the horses hanging in the air. The crisp feeling of winter. The frosty air filling their lungs.

Fritz Hanson, with a fur cap and coat, sat in the driver's seat quietly puffing on his pipe.

With his big mittens he pulled gently on the reins and yelled, "Hi there! Git-up you Snitzel Fritters! Haw-ya!"

The sleigh moved easily across the snow.

The trip through the woods had class. The artist had painted a white cover over everything— the trees, the fence, the posts. How unique he was in his work using the snow in his landscape.

The well groomed trail that carried the big sleigh was cut right through the woods. As the jacks passed by the huge tree trunks they felt like they were in another world. The wind spun by and sent up a cloud of snow high in the air.

Fritz pulled up on the reins and yelled, "Whoa Boy!" and the big Belgian animals came to a stop.

There were piles of logs everywhere. Big logs. Small logs. All stacked neatly in a pile. In fact, they resembled the walls of a house. Rows of logs like a family dwelling. A cozy shelter. A hidden retreat. All standing high and silent. No sound at all except for the voices of the lumberjacks. Then there was the call of "TIMBERRR" ! ! ! A short pause came before the giant tree came tumbling down. The thunderous explosion rocked the ground like a giant quake. It kicked up dust like a violent tornado. Then, the earth settled down for a gentle rest.

The lumberjacks all climbed out of the sleigh and stretched their legs before going to work.

CHAPTER 11

Peter Muirhead was the foreman or the pusher as some would say. He lined up his men to work in groups known as crews.

The crew that Danny was assigned to had just cut down a huge pine tree. It must have been three foot across. Now came the big job of cutting it up into twenty foot lengths.

After the first cut Danny was impressed, "Holy smoke! Look at all those rings! Why, there must be a hundred of 'em!"

Jessie Jones was disturbed, "What's so great about that? It's just another tree."

"I was just impressed by all those rings."

"Hey kid! Just shut up and get to work!"

"I know it's my first day. I guess I talk too much."

"You better believe it, kid!"

"Well, I'll try to do better."

"You better shape up, kid and close your trap. Start carrying your weight around here!"

"I am carrying my own weight! What's it to

you?"

"You just don't know from Adam!"

"What do you mean by that? You ain't my boss!"

"No, and it's a good thing I ain't! You wouldn't last one minute if I was. You green kid!"

"Hey! What do ya' mean by that?"

"You're just a mama's boy. You're still wet behind the ears."

"Hey! Who are you calling a mama's boy? You're just an old has-been."

"Hey! That settles it! Push me around will ya'?! Put up or shut up!"

With that Danny made a mistake. He swung at Jessie and missed. Jessie came back with a blow to Danny's head that stunned him. Again Danny swung at Jessie and missed. Then, Jessie got rough. He hit Danny with a left in the stomach and a right to the chin. Danny was gasping for breath. He bent over and fell to the ground.

Jessie spouted off, "Look kid! Nobody talks to me that way! Nobody!"

Jessie then went over and kicked the kid in the stomach.

At that point Jack Manley stepped in. He was a big Swede they called Preacher. He was really an ex-prize fighter who read the Scripture.

He spoke up, "Hey! What's going on here?"

Jessie snarled back, "It ain't none of your damn business, Preacher. Just buzz off."

"Hey boy! I don't believe this. You beat up that young kid?"

"He bugged me. He talked too much."

"Well, now ain't that a shame! I really feel for ya'!"

"Hey man, don't do me no favors!"

"Don't worry, I won't. You're the one who's in trouble, not me."

"Just keep out of this, will ya'?"

Jack reached over and grabbed hold of Jessie's shoulder and with that Jessie swung around and hit him in the face. The blood ran down Jack's nose, and he wiped it off with the back of his hand.

Jessie spouted off, "Hey big man! You're not so big now!"

Jessie again swung at Jack and this time clipped him on the chin. Jack bit his lip and then let go with everything he had. He pumped a left and right into Jessie's stomach. Jessie staggered back and looked surprised. He then moved in with both fists hammering away at Jessie's ribs. Jessie kept throwing punches and missing. Jack bent over like a professional with both fists up circling his prey, waiting for him to make his move. Then, the urge hit him and he flew at Jessie like a madman. Jessie backed away confused. It was then that Jack stumbled and fell to one knee. Jessie's corked boot caught him on the chin and then poked him on the left arm. That's when Jack grabbed Jessie by the leg and twisted. He could hear the bone snap as

Jessie let out an ungodly yell. Jack knew at that point he had broken his leg.

By this time the whole camp had formed a big circle around the two fighting men. They were yelling and cheering and giving out all kinds of advice, "Hit him again! Knock him down! Put the boots to him!"

Peter arrived at the scene and pushed through the crowd. When he saw the two fighters, he threw up his hands in disgust.

He spouted off, "Hey, you jacks! What in God's name do you think you're doing? Let's break it up and get back to work! We got some logs to run! Come on now, let's move it!"

The men reacted and started moving away.

Jack just stood there looking down at the disabled figure below.

He thought to himself, "What have I done? Why did I do it?"

His hands started shaking, and the sweat was running down his cheeks.

He looked up into the heavens and said, "Forgive me, Lord, for I know not what I am doing. Excuse my conduct. Forgive my action. Change my behavior. The Devil has taken over my body. He has given me hate. He has given me malice. He has given me pain. Give me the strength to make amends. To improve my life. To change my ways."

He ended his request by saying, "Lord! Why me?"

CHAPTER 12

Mary Johnson hears tall tales from the woods as David explains, "I would sometimes work late at night in my office at the logging camp. I would look out the window at the bunkhouse across the way. The little building had icicles hanging down and no windows. I would wonder what the gang inside was doing?"

Inside, Blackjack Ralph spoke up, "Let's see now, we'll roll that old keg over here and put this here piece of wood on top, and we've got ourselves a table!"

Buckskin Bill then asked, "Hey, Blackjack, did you really work in one of them big gambling houses out west?"

Blackjack replied, "Yup, sure did! Why, some of those cowpokes would come in there with their pockets loaded with money. They were just beggin' me to take it off their hands. So, I'd obliged 'em. It just seemed to be the proper thing to do!"

Buckskin mumbled, "Gosh! It sure does sound excitin'!"

Blackjack then pulled out an old deck of cards and sounded off, "Now, come on you jacks, pull those boxes over here to sit on, and we'll start right off with five card stud."

Buckskin asked, "What stakes are we playin' fer?"

Blackjack bit his lip and then added, "The stakes will be a penny a point. Now, I'll deal one card down and one card up."

Not everybody played cards. Dynamite Jim was darning his socks, and Hobo Harry was washing out his long johns.

Then there was another group who just enjoyed telling stories.

Big Foot Willy could wait no longer, "I'll never forget the time when I was working in the Manistique Camp. We had a big old foreman called "Penny." He was a likeable kind of cuss, but when it came to stackin' logs, he sure was a pusher. He used to stack them logs higher than a church steeple. Yes sir, you'd walk through those piles of logs like you were in some kind of village. It sorta' gave ya' the creeps though lookin' up at them babies and wonderin' what would happen if they ever let go!"

Applejack Pete who was drawing on his pipe finally spoke, "Yeah, I can remember one time when I was up in the Seney Camp. We'd been workin' all mornin', and we had cleared the woods out pretty good. There were trees layin' everywhere, and I mean everywhere. There were some of them babies six feet in diameter. They'd just throw a chain around them logs and that team of Belgins would slid them babies right up on a sleigh just as slick as you please!"

High Pockets Joe was quiet for a spell and then had this to say, "I can remember a feller by the name of 'Pete'!

"Nobody knew if he had a second name or not. I'll tell ya' one thing though, that man could really pull a saw. He was just a little dude but that didn't stop him. I don't know where the old goat got his strength, but he sure could grind away at that wood. Do you know somethin'? When he started sawing away, that there sawdust would start building up. It would build up higher than a kite!"

Montana Slim started yawning and then shook his head and sputtered, "I don't know about you guys but I reckon I'm gonna' have to turn in. I'm gettin' mighty tired. I just can't keep my eyes open."

Someone would blow out the kerosene lamp and after a few minutes you could hear heavy breathing and then snoring.

Mary Johnson explained it this way. They were just little boys in a big man's fantasy. They were both good and bad. Rough and tough. Gentle and kind. They had a unique characteristic. They were both genuine and real. Sincere and natural. They were all SAINTS in a LUMBERJACK WORLD.

CHAPTER 13

David decided to go on a surveying trip into northern California. He left his bookkeeper and foreman in charge while he was gone.

Peter Muirhead stumped across the yard and went up the steps into the kitchen. He was upset, and the bubbles of sweat stood out on his forehead. He glared at a man in a white hat who was stirring a large pot of soup on the stove.

Peter snarled, "You're Roy Snider, the cook, ain't cha'?"

Roy looked around calmly and admitted, "I sure am!"

"Well, what I wanna' know is where the hell is this guy Tommy Ram?" Peter growled.

"I don't know what you're stewing about?" Roy muttered as he continued stirring the soup.

"I gotta' get ahold of this here guy Tommy. They told me he was with you!"

Roy stirring with a wooden spoon explained, "He went into town with me this afternoon to get supplies!"

"Well, I wanna' git my hands on that guy!" Peter stormed.

Roy spun around and laid the wooden spoon on the counter.

He picked up a cleaver as he spoke, "I don't care WHO you are or WHAT you're after, but when you come into MY kitchen, I'M the boss! I'M in charge here, so get your TAIL outta' here!"

Peter stared in amazement, "I gotta' get this guy. Nobody has whisky in my camp and I'm gonna' find him!"

Roy swung the cleaver around and drove it hard into a wooden block on the counter and roared, "He went into town with me and I ain't seen him since!"

Peter drew back confused, "I thought he was in here with you! Do you know where he's got the bottle?"

Roy took a deep breath and then let it out, "He helped me load supplies at the store. He said he had to go to the toilet and he'd meet me out front of the Saloon. I paid my bill at the store and picked him up out front. Everything seemed all right to me. He got in the wagon and we came back to camp. That's all I know!"

Peter left the kitchen and went over to the bunk house. He thought he might find Tommy there. Sure enough, when he opened the door Tommy was sitting on his bunk.

"So THERE ya' are! I've been looking for ya'!"

Peter bellered as he moved into the room.

"Oh, hello Peter!" Tommy answered.

"I wantcha' to get your FANNY out of here, RIGHT NOW!" Peter stormed.

Tommy said meekly, "What do you mean?"

Peter growled, "You know DAMNED WELL what I mean!"

Tommy apologizing, "I was sick. My stomach was actin' up so I took the afternoon off!"

Peter pointing his finger, "You violated the rules of the camp, and you've got to go!"

Tommy went on, "When I came back to the bunkhouse, I saw Roy who was going into town for supplies. I asked him if I could go along to help?"

Peter shaking his finger blurted out, "Look Sonny Boy, NOBODY has whisky in my camp so get your TAIL outta' here! PRONTO!"

Tommy continued, "I brought a bottle back because I thought it would help my stomach!"

Peter angrily spouted off, "Look! Get your things together 'cause if you're not outta' here when I come back I'll THROW ya' out! Do ya' HEAR me?"

Peter turned and left through the door. Tommy just stood there for a minute, and then he reached under his pillow and pulled out a bottle of whisky and took a drink. You could hear the liquid gurgle as it went down his throat. He straightened the bottle up and popped on the cork. He held the bottle up and spoke to it, "You're my pal! You're my buddy! You're my friend! You're won'erful!"

He laid the bottle down on the bed and talked to the wall, "Peter! You got a lot to learn! You don't know from nothin'! You just can't fire a man fer no reason! No reason at all! Just fer takin' a little old drink! It ain't fair! It ain't right!"

He wiped his mouth off with the back of his hand and then growled, "I'll leave the camp for now, but I'll be back. You ain't heard the last of me, Peter! I'll be back and I'll get even!"

CHAPTER 14

Peter ate a late supper in the cookshack that night. The kerosene lamps were glowing when he left the dining room.

As he walked down the dark path, he started mumbling to himself, "The big boss always wanted to know how many logs were cut, and I got that information right here in my pocket."

He stopped mumbling as he moved out into the night. He made his way down the path and around the supply shed. At that point he felt the presence of someone behind him. Before he could turn around, a figure grabbed him and thrust a knife into his side. Peter felt the sharp jab as the blade went in. He could sense the pain and felt the hot blood on his fingers. A fatal charge went through his entire body as he slumped to the ground. He thought about his youth. He was stronger than the rest. He could withstand pain. He could endure suffering. He could stand torture. He was tough. He was hard. He could outlast any of them. He was very weak now and out of control. The icy snow chilled his face as he blacked out.

CHAPTER 15

When David returned from his surveying trip Gary was waiting for him outside his office.

Gary said eagerly, "I've got something to tell you!"

David answered, "Let's go inside!"

Gary told him about Peter being stabbed and that he was taken to the hospital. Also, that Tommy Ram was arrested and put in jail. He said the doctor told him that Peter was a very lucky man. If the knife had gone in any deeper, Peter wouldn't have made it.

David spouted! "PRAISE THE LORD! PRAISE THE LORD!"

When Peter got out of the hospital, he went straight to the camp office.

When he pushed open the door, David was there to greet him, "Peter! How are you, you OLD SON OF A GUN?"

Peter replied, "Oh, I'm all right! You know you can't keep an old jack like me down. I always bounce back!"

David agreed, "Good! Come on in and find a chair!"

Peter went over and sat down.

David continued, "You know Gary, our bookkeeper, who works here in the office?"

Peter nodded, "Sure, I know Gary!"

David went on, "I've got a few items I want to talk to you about. As you know, the market for logs is slowing down. The demand for lumber is declining. It's just like everything else. When you have an abundance of one thing, the price goes down. This means we've got to finish our cut and get it ready for the mill at a faster rate. We're going to have to speed up our operations. We're going to have to cut out the fool play and push the men a little harder. We're going to have to get more pine out."

Gary spoke up, "As bookkeeper I find a lot of the men quitting lately. I guess they are going to other camps. We've got to stop them and try to hold on to them or we'll have no work force at all." David broke in, "That's where you come in, Peter!

"You've got to stop these men from leaving and going to other camps."

Peter took a deep breath and then let it out, "All right. I'll do what I can but they're not going to like it! I've got some darn good men out there! I've got the best doggone crews in the business, and I hate to lose 'em by putting the pressure on 'em! I'm afraid they'll quit!"

David spoke in that soft voice again, "Gary has come up with a plan. I'll let him tell you about it."

Gary cleared his throat and then swallowed deeply and explained, "O.K., here's my plan: If a man remains with us until the cut is finished or until spring break, he gets his full pay. If he quits early and attempts to draw his wages early, he will be penalized. We will take fifty cents a month penalty out of his earnings."

Peter's face got red, and he began to get mad. Suddenly, he exploded, "He WON'T like it! He'll think we're CHEATIN' him! I know my men and they're not going to take it! You mark my word, they're not going to like it ONE DAMN BIT!"

David stood up from his chair and spoke, "Well, that's the way it will have to be. We'll try it out and see how it goes. Maybe we'll have to change it later on but for now give it a try."

Peter got up, put his hat on and started mumbling to himself as he went out. He left the camp office and moved on down the road. He finally came to the location where one of his crews was working.

Bennie Rogers, the head chopper, was swinging his axe at the base of a huge tree.

Peter spoke up, "That's a lot of wood!"

Bennie answered, "They don't come any bigger!"

Bennie took great pride in the smoothness of his undercut. The "V" groove was finished now, so Bennie stopped chopping. He only had to scar the other side and she'd start to tilt.

Tony Olson, another jack, decided to venture out into the space where the giant pine would drop. He thought it would fall right about there in the empty space, between the aspen and the beechwood.

Then came the call "TIMBERRR!!!"

He heard the call but didn't turn fast enough. His feet were frozen. He was paralyzed. He was unable to move. He saw the top dropping in his direction, but his legs were numb. A wet sweat covered his forehead. The hostile green pine needles were then all around him. He felt a burning in his chest. He couldn't breath. He was suffocating. A cold chill came over his entire body. A dull feeling was inside him, and then he blacked out. He was gone. Gone from the face of the earth. Gone to another world.

The crew all came running to try to free him from the massive tree. They started chopping away at the branches, but it was no use. Tony had died in the crash.

Mary Johnson felt the pain. She wrote, "For all the boughs that crushed him there was a feeling of contempt. Against the pine. Against the big forest. Against all of the wilderness. He was just another SAINT that was lost in the black forest of the white pine."

CHAPTER 16

When the lakes began to thaw and spring was in the air, it was time. Time for a log drive. All the logs that had been stacked so neatly in the winter time now had to be floated down stream to the mill.

Billy Mack and Marty Jackson were the best darn log drivers ever until they met Jerry Smith. The three of them worked as the number one team when the big log drive moved into high gear. These jacks could do anything and everything on the back of a floating log. There was no feat they couldn't perform. They also had quite a reputation for their barroom brawls. When some of the drunken jacks would become mean and belligerent they would step right in and help the barkeep escort them out.

The big thing now was the log drive. The sun was high in the sky and it was a real bright morning. They all wore backpacks on their backs which contained food and other supplies for the trip.

They met at the river bank on that special day when the logs were being rolled into the water. Each man carried a big cant hook which he would use to keep his balance and also free the log jams. They all stepped out on the big log jam at the same time. They stood like captains on the bridge of a ship leaving the harbor.

All the logs started moving along over the dam and into the narrow channel. The cleats on the bottom of their boots dug into the wet logs and held them in place like a fly on a shiny window glass.

They watched the trees go by as the current carried them on the flow through the dense forest on both sides. They were now on their way down the highway of adventure which was to be a wild trip.

They had been traveling along for about an hour when a big twenty-footer moved across the channel and hooked into a tree hanging over the bank. This backed up the whole pack creating a huge log jam. Billy quickly stepped from log to log over to where the log was hung up. Using his cant hook he moved the log free, and the drive continued on.

After another hour of moving down stream, Billy, who was in the lead, decided it was lunch time. He moved the lead log over to one side and locked it into the bank. This stopped the flow of logs so he could step off onto the river bank. He looked back and motioned to the others to follow. They were also hungry, so there was no hesitation.

Billy found a grassy patch and slid out of his backpack. He flipped open the pocket and pulled out a sandwich. In the middle of his second sandwich, he started munching on an apple.

He paused for a minute and then spoke, "When the drive is over, I think I'll settle down for awhile."

He took the last bite out of his apple and threw the core into the woods.

"Yeah, it's been a hard winter," Marty added as he leaned back against a big tree. "I think the first thing I'm gonna' do is order one of them there big steaks at Harry's Restaurant." he stated as he put his hands behind his head and leaned back to rest.

Jerry had another idea. He spoke up, "You know after this whole drive is over I'm gonna' climb into a hot tub at the boarding house. Then, I'll make my way over to the Paradise Saloon and meet Mildred."

The other two in unison blurted out, "Oh sure, MILDRED! Don't forget MILDRED!"

Jerry continued, "I saw her the other night when she was dancing. She sure is a wiggler. She was strutting round the stage when Big Red grabbed her arm. That sucker wouldn't let go. Well, I wasn't gonna' stand fer that! I got a bear hug around his neck and shut off his wind. He finally let go, but then look out! He came after me with them big knuckles of his. It took me quite a spell to settle him down. I had to pin him to the floor. That's when I found out the owner weren't none too happy either. That's when he threw us both out in the street! That's the thanks I get for trying to keep the peace!"

Marty had a big grin on his face as he picked up a stone and threw it into the water.

Billy stretched out his legs and then announced, "Well, I guess we better get this here show on the road!"

He got up and put his half of a sandwich back into his backpack and slipped it on. He was ready to go and so were the others. They all stepped out on the log jam, and when Billy unlocked the lead plug, the logs all started moving again.

The logs were all shiny, wet, and very slippery. Billy caught himself once as he started to fall.

He thought to himself, "You better sharpen up and stay alert and not lose your balance."

As the logs bounced sideways against each other, their sharp movement threw him off balance again. He bent his knees for support.

Suddenly, the logs started bouncing up and down as they approached a down hill rapids. They started moving at a faster pace.

Billy thought to himself, "Hold onto your hat, Billy, 'cause things are getting rough!"

Billy remembered another time when he was a kid. It was in the winter time. He stood on a sled holding onto a rope when he went down a hill. He went flying through the air and almost killed himself.

A jerk to the right made him dig in his corked

boots. He bent his legs apart to reduce the shock. The logs were moving fast now swinging in a right and left motion. It was almost like the Devil himself was trying to knock him off. The logs all followed in line around a bend in the river with uncontrollable force. He rode free as the wind as they bounced and turned and finally settled down into a quiet lagoon. They floated down endlessly into quiet waters. It was like an act of God. A strange achievement. An unreal behavior. A spiritual encounter. Everything suddenly seemed peaceful and quiet. It was the end of the line.

He glanced around to see how the others were doing. Marty was the only one he could see. He wondered what had happened to Jerry? He wondered if he was all right. He broke out into a cold sweat when he found out that Jerry didn't make it. He had fallen between two big logs, and they had crushed his skull.

A chill came over his entire body. He thought of himself. His restlessness. His agitation. His frenzy. The desire he had for excitement. Doing the impossible. His conquest for victory. The raging battle to conquer. This could have been him. He could have taken the wrong step. He could have lost his balance. It could have been him between the logs. His stomach was churning. His heart was pounding. His head was spinning. He suddenly felt real sick inside.

Mary Johnson tells it like it is. "The troubled

waters were both savage and fierce. Mad and insane. It was all a game of chance. A gamble to stay alive. They had to be fearless and brave. Gutsy and daring. They all embarked on a mission impossible. Their lives were in jeopardy. Their souls were in danger. Yet, they made the whole thing happen. They made it all possible. They were loggers. All SAINTS that traveled down the treacherous river of no return."

CHAPTER 17

Billy Mack spoke up, "Mr. Ward, I've been talking with the men, and since this is our last Saturday night before spring break, we'd like to celebrate and have a party."

David agreed, "That sounds like a good idea. There is just one thing, you can't have it here in the camp because we don't allow any whisky. It's a camp rule."

Billy answered, "Oh, I'm sorry! We just thought it would be a nice gesture to get together for one last time."

David replied, "I agree with you. Yes, I think that's a fine idea. I'll tell what we'll do. I'll furnish a wagon to take you into town. I'll even buy you all a drink and stake you to a meal as a farewell gesture.

Billy responded, "Oh, that would be great!"

David went on, "There's just one thing. I've got some business I've got to attend to, so I'll be unable to go. But Gary, my bookkeeper might volunteer?"

Gary added, "Sure! I'll be glad to take them. We'll go into town, I'll buy them a couple of drinks, we'll get something to eat, and then we'll come home. It seems harmless enough!"

David remarked, "Yeah! It seems harmless enough!"

When they first came into town, they saw two men fighting in the street. A crowd had gathered around the men and they were cheering them on. The men were punching and jabbing at each other. Suddenly, one grabbed the other and bit off part of his ear. The crowd all cheered at the sight of blood. This made the other jack mad, and he kicked him in the stomach.

Gary looked away in despair, "That's DISGUSTING! That's TERRIBLE! That's the most disgusting THING I've EVER seen! Come on you men, let's go inside!"

They all entered the Paradise Saloon by going through the swinging doors.

When they got inside Gary told the barkeep, "I'd like to buy drinks for my friends here!"

He laid a ten dollar bill on the counter.

The barkeep, smiling, answered, "Sure thing! They're comin' right up!"

Andy, a little old man sitting at the bar spoke up, "I asked for another drink! He wouldn't give it to me! The barkeep says, "You've had enough!" Who the HELL is he to tell ME I've had enough? I should know, not HIM! Then, that other feller buys drinks for everybody. It just AIN'T right! No sir, it just AIN'T right!"

Billy blurted out, "I think you've had enough, old man!"

Andy answered, "Who the HELL are you? What do YOU know about it?"

Billy added, "Hey! You better back off!"

Andy came back, "I ain't gonna' back off!"

Billy spouted, "You better!"

Andy paused to meditate. He started mumbling to himself, "I ain't backin' down! I ain't givin' in! I ain't givin' up! I ain't gonna' talk about it....No MORE!!!"

Andy made his move. He struck Billy in the nose. Billy responded by pushing him backwards. He fell into a table where four Jacks were sitting. That's all it took. It was like a bell had gone off. The WHOLE place erupted. Fists were flying! Jacks were howling! There was pushing and shoving! Punching and hitting! An uppercut to the chin! A poke in the stomach. A hit on the head! A brass cuspidor banged against the wall! A body was thrown through a window! Chairs were being broken! Tables were demolished'. The smell of stale beer, dirty sweat and fowl smoke saturated the air......and still the gala event went on!

CHAPTER 18

David came into the camp office and was greeted by Roy Snider, the camp cook.

David spoke, "Good morning, Roy! How are things in the kitchen?"

Roy paused and then answered, "I don't know! It just seems exceptionally quiet!"

David was puzzled, "What do you mean?"

Roy answered, "I don't know. I can't tell you why? It just doesn't seem right! I was getting ready to cook breakfast when I got that funny feeling. There was nobody to cook for. There was nobody in camp!"

Peter came into the office with a white face like he'd seen a ghost. He went over to a chair and fell into it.

David leaned over the desk and asked, "What's wrong?"

Peter folded his hands and then announced, "Boss! We've got a problem?" His hands were shaking as he muttered, "The men didn't show up for work this mornin'! It's not just one or two but the whole KIT-AND-CABOODLE!" There's not a SOUL out there! It's down right SPOOKY!"

David in disbelief, "Wait a minute! You mean nobody's working?"

"That's right! Not a dad-ratted soul! I got up this mornin' feelin' fine and when I got to the cookshack nobody was around! It's like a morgue!"

Roy broke in, "That's right! I got the same feeling. Nobody's here!"

David thought for a minute, "This is serious. How can this be?"

Peter took a deep breath and then added, "I went into town with the lads Saturday night when they had their party. They were all having a good time, so I left and came back to camp. I don't know why they're not here!"

David grabbed his coat and hat and sputtered, "Come on Peter, let's you and me go into town and find out what has happened!"

When they approached the town, all seemed quiet and still. A lazy dog walked slowly across the street.

Peter pointed to the Paradise Saloon and confirmed, "That's the place! That's where the boys were when I left!"

The place seemed empty except for a young boy who was sweeping the floor. David moved over to the bar and sat on a stool.

The barkeep entered from the back and asked, "Do you want somethin'?"

"I SURE do!" David answered as he leaned on the counter. "I'm David Ward from the Ward Lumber Camp, and this is my foreman Peter. I came here looking for my lumberjacks. They were celebrating in here Saturday night and they have disappeared!"

The barkeep cleared his throat and then spoke, "Yeah, I remember that bunch. They told me that they were from your camp. They were the guys who got involved in a brawl we had here. It turned into a pretty big fight."

"Do you know what happened to them?" David inquired as he stared at the man.

The barkeep bit his lip and then explained, "After the fight I think they all went over to the Royal. It's a big hotel on the hill."

David thanked the man, and the two of them left through the swinging doors.

The Royal was a popular place. David knew about the reputation it had for loose woman. He knew he was in for some trouble.

As they approached the front door, an attractive young girl wiggled her hips and then walked up to greet them.

"Hi there fellas, are you looking for a good time?" she reported as she smiled and motioned back at the hotel.

David becoming impatient spoke up, "We want to see the owner. Do you know if he's in?"

The smile left her face as she answered, "Yeah,

I just saw him. He's in the lobby." The two men walked up the steps and went inside.

The Royal was quiet now with nobody around except the hotel clerk behind the desk. David asked him about the manager and before the clerk could answer a big man, who looked like a wrestler, moved over to the desk.

He looked over at David and snarled, "Do you guys want somethin'?"

David who was very serious responded, "We want to see the manager!"

The big man spouted off, "Well, you see he's busy right now! You'll have to come back another time!"

The big man pulled out a pair of black gloves and proceeded in putting them on.

A voice from the backroom blurted out, "That's all right, Jake, I'll take care of it!"

A man, who was dressed in a fancy suit, appeared, wearing a red tie with a white carnation popping out of his breast lapel. He motioned for them to come over to a door where he was standing. "I'm Bart Star, owner of the hotel. Come into my office!" he ordered as he motioned for them to go inside.

Bart went behind his desk and pointed to chairs and advised, "Have a seat gentlemen!"

David walked over and stood by one of the chairs and spoke, "I'm David Ward, owner of a lumber camp, and I've got a problem?"

"What's that?" Bart asked as he folded his hands on his desk.

"It seems my men came into town Saturday night and I want to know what happened to them!"

"Well, that is a problem!"

"The barkeep at the Paradise said my men came over here after they left the saloon. Do you know anything about that?"

"Well, we have so many people coming in here it's hard to say."

"Well, I want to find out right away if my men are here?"

"Well, as a matter of fact, your men were involved in a fight, and they became violent and unruly and they had to be put in jail."

"MY MEN are in JAIL!"

"I took care of that. I paid their fines, and I got them out!"

"Where are they now? I came to get them!"

"Not so fast! You see I got them out of jail, so now they belong to me!"

David shaking his head in amazement replied, "I don't believe this! You say my men BELONG to you?"

Bart, smiling, bragged, "That's right! I own them now!"

David sat down in a chair and quietly spoke, "You know, Bart, I've heard a lot about you, and I've been wanting to meet you. One thing, you are running your organization under false colors. Your whole operation is wrong. For one thing the land you've built your empire on was never purchased legally from the U.S. Government. This land is not yours! It's not paid for!"

The smile left Bart's face as he spoke, "What do you mean?"

David, smiling, advised, "If you'll release my men I won't say anything about this to the U.S. Government."

Bart said, "You drive a hard bargain. I'll see what I can do."

The next day all the men were back in camp. Life continued on as usual. The men were paid their wages and the camp closed down, as planned, for the spring break.

CHAPTER 19

Back at the camp office, Mary Johnson, the newspaper reporter, had been writing down the highlights of David's life.

Mary looked over at David and spoke, "You sure have lived a very interesting life!" David replied, "Yes! A lot has happened."

Mary closed her notebook and stood up. "You've answered my question! I know now why you went into the lumber business! There's something about the woods! It grows on you. It becomes a part of your life. You fall in love with it."

Mary held out her hand to David and remarked, "I'm glad I met you Mr. Ward!"

David jumped to his feet and shook her hand.

Mary turned and her high top shoes clicked on the hardwood floor as she moved toward the big oak door. She opened it, turned, and waved good-bye before she went out.

Outside, she paused on the porch and looked out into the woods. The trees meant more to her now. They seemed to have a mind of their own. Their green foliage seemed to be calling to her. She could hear the soft wind blowing through their boughs. They seemed to make a music of their own. She could feel the floor of the forest beneath her feet. Their branches tearing away at her sides. She could sense the huge roots holding up the giant structures. Solid as a rock. Hard as nails. Firm as steel. All anchored so firm into the ground they never move. They never change. They'll always be there. They would last forever except....man has HIS say. Then, their trunks come tumbling down. The whole span of events takes on a different meaning. The forest becomes an open space. A giant stump is left as a marker of what used to be. That's all that's left of the image of the mighty tree. She now could hear the voices of the lumberjacks talking in the wind. She could hear their mighty axes chopping away at the wood. Then, the wind died down and all was quiet. All was still. A kind of hush came over the woods like an act of God. She walked down the steps and climbed into her buggy and down the road she went. Just like the finale at the end of a grand performance.

CHAPTER 20

Mary Johnson wrote the last page of her news story.

David Ward finally retired from the lumber business. He moved to his orchard lake home near Detroit where he lived out the rest of his days. He still bought land and property whenever the price was right. Then, on the 29th day of May in the year 1900, David Ward died peacefully in his sleep.

Outside his bedroom window stood a small green pine. The structure marked a symbol of his achievements. His hardships in the woods. The sweat and strain of sore muscles. The struggle for survival. The exertion and the pain. The cold bitter mornings when the air was crisp. The deafening sound when a massive tree came thundering down. The saws grinding away at the wood. The sour smell of wet sap. The massive logs stacked sky high moving gracefully across an icy road. That's the voice of the forest. That's what the lumbering age was all about.

The lumberjacks were the backbone of the

whole event. The fantastic acts they achieved. The dangerous feats they performed. The unique behavior they expressed. I'm sure a guardian angel must have been watching over them in their attempt to conquer the black forest.

I look out my window at the open space next door. They are building a house there now. They are constructing a new home. The carpenters are fitting in each piece of wood. It's all taking shape. It's all coming together. It's all a reality. A beautiful creation. A lovely work of art. A family dwelling. It's all made possible. Possible, because of them.

I look up into the heavens as I speak to God Almighty, "I'm sure St. Peter, will be waiting at the Golden Gate, WHEN THE SAINTS COME MARCHING IN."